WHY ALWAYS WINS

STAY CURIOUS!

STEPHEN GAY

ILLUSTRATIONS BY DER-SHING HELMER

CONTENTS

INTRODUCTION

RON KERTZNER

How many times have you worked on team projects where you may have gotten the results you wanted but have little or no desire to work with the people on that project again!? Or, where the relationships on the team were so toxic you actually didn't get the results you needed? Or, you just felt lousy about yourself, lousy about the team, completely dispirited and exhausted?

All too often in our current need for speed, we tend to focus exclusively on the results we are trying to create without regard to who we are working with, how the work gets done, and why we are working together. It's as if we are driving a car at 80 miles per hour without truly understanding how the car works.

Why Always Wins offers a fun and informative understanding of the mechanics needed to work collaboratively. The engine that fuels collaborative work is awareness: self awareness, social awareness, and team awareness. In other words, in order to focus effectively on our work, we need to develop a conscious awareness of the context. What is going on internally that may affect my participation or collaboration? What are the dynamics of the team I am working with? How do culture, group behavior, and regional/global differences influence how we work together?

Over the past 30 years, I've had the opportunity to work with thousands of people to help build this muscle of awareness. This muscle building enables people to make conscious choices that lead to meaningful results. Without an opportunity to reflect on these levels of awareness, we often rush headlong into projects unconsciously. We act out of old habits, conditioned ways of thinking, and emotional reactions. And, when things don't work out, it becomes all too easy to blame others—or get dejected and put all the blame on ourselves.

The conscious choices we make can facilitate the experience of flow, a mental and emotional state of operation in which teams are fully immersed in what they are doing, characterized by a feeling of energized focus, full involvement, and success in the process of the activity. Other ways of describing this experience are "being in the zone," "operating at our optimal capacity," and "totally enjoying what we are doing while getting sh—t done!"

You often hear sports stars or musicians talk about being in the zone and the impact it has on their team. In the book *The Fifth Discipline*, MIT professor Peter Senge quotes Bill Russell, the legendary center for the Boston Celtics, about this experience. "Every so often a Celtics game would heat up so that it became more than a physical or even mental game and would be magical. The feeling is difficult to describe...When it happened I could feel my play rise to a new level...The game would move so fast that every fake, cut, and pass would be surprising, and yet nothing could surprise me. It was almost as if we were playing in slow motion. During those spells, I could almost sense how the next play would develop and where the next shot would be taken...To me, the key was that both teams had to be playing at their peaks..."

My sense is that we've all had experiences of being in the flow with teams when everyone was playing at their peaks. While Bill Russell describes this experience as magical, it is useful to ask what mindsets, skills, and behaviors increase the likelihood of individuals and teams being in the flow.

Why Always Wins offers a great start. Through a mindset of being curious about what is taking place in ourselves, how to better understand the people we are working with, and how to best achieve outcomes together, we can begin to create the conditions that facilitate high-performance teams that produce great results.

And like great teams experience in all sorts of human endeavors, according to Bill Russell, "success is a result of the consistent practice of winning skills and attitudes." **Why Always Wins**, through its creative exploration of mindfulness, emotional triggers, flexing to other people's styles, balancing advocacy and inquiry, facilitating teams to move from "I" to "we," gaining clarity and shared vision on goals, and creating a culture of "yes," provides a roadmap for these skills and attitudes.

Why Always Wins is all about rediscovering the inherent joy that comes when we individually bring our best in concert with others. It's all about the flow.

SEVENTY-SIX DEGREES AND SUNNY.

ANOTHER MONDAY MORNING IN THE VALLEY.

EVERYONE'S IN SUCH A RUSH AROUND HERE. IT'S ALL, BETTER HURRY UP AND CHANGE THE WORLD!

AND THAT'S WHY I TOOK THIS JOB. I WANTED TO DO SOMETHING THAT MATTERS.

13

CHAPTER 1

INVEST IN RELATIONSHIPS

A critical investment in your career will be the relationships you nurture with your coworkers and leadership. By developing a deep understanding of **team dynamics** and **social awareness**, you'll build a foundation for strengthening key relationships and maintaining **team flow**. To understand others, you'll need to understand yourself, which involves identifying and controlling your **personal triggers**.

LET'S HOPE AMIT GOT THE NEW SNAP-BETA PROTOTYPE DONE.

I PROMISED I'D SHOW IT AT THE TEAM MEETING THIS AFTERNOON.

HEY, AMIT.

HOW WAS YOUR WEEKEND?

WEEKEND?

I DON'T BELIEVE IN WEEKENDS.

RIGHT. SO ARE YOU READY TO SHARE THE BETA SCREENS?

SURE AM.

I GOT ALL OF THE CLICK TARGETS WORKING.

NOT ONLY THAT, BUT I ADDED A COUPLE OF EXTRA FEATURES.

REVISION 3a

header

Lorem ipsum dolor ame

LOOK, MAX.

I DON'T THINK ANYONE'S GONNA NOTICE THE DIFFERENCE.

I WILL! YOU CAN'T JUST SLAP RANDOM COLORS ALL OVER OUR PRODUCT.

THE NEW COLORS MAKE IT EASIER TO USE.

AMIT–!

WELL, I'M GONNA GO BACK TO CODING.

RIGHT. I HAVE A MEETING.

19

AM I THE ONLY ONE WHO CARES ABOUT DESIGN?

THIS IS EXACTLY WHY WE CAN'T GET ANYTHING DONE AROUND HERE!

WAIT, MAX! DO YOU HAVE THE LATEST LOGIN SCREEN SPECS?

YEAH, HOLD ON.

WAIT, THIS ISN'T MY FLASH DRIVE.

I GUESS SOMEONE ELSE DIDN'T JOIN THE CLOUD REVOLUTION.

I'LL GET YOU THE FILE ASAP.

SUCCESSFUL COMPANIES KNOW THAT HIGH-PERFORMING TEAMS ARE A COMPETITIVE ADVANTAGE.

THIS TYPICALLY EQUATES TO HIGHER REVENUES AND LONG-TERM COMPANY SUCCESS.

TO BUILD A HIGH-PERFORMING TEAM REQUIRES BOTH AWARENESS AND UNDERSTANDING OF YOURSELF AND OTHERS.

LEADERSHIP CAN LEARN TOOLS AND TECHNIQUES TO NURTURE HIGH-PERFORMING TEAMS, BUT TEAMWORK CAN'T BE BOUGHT.

IT REQUIRES THE COURAGE OF INDIVIDUALS TO START BUILDING STRONG RELATIONSHIPS AND TO CREATE A SENSE OF TRUST.

THAT MAKES SENSE!

THE POWER OF TEAMWORK CAN'T BE DENIED. TRUST IS THE FOUNDATION OF ANY GREAT TEAM.

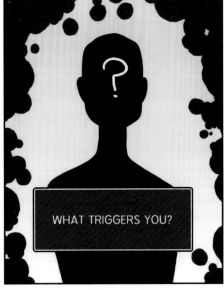

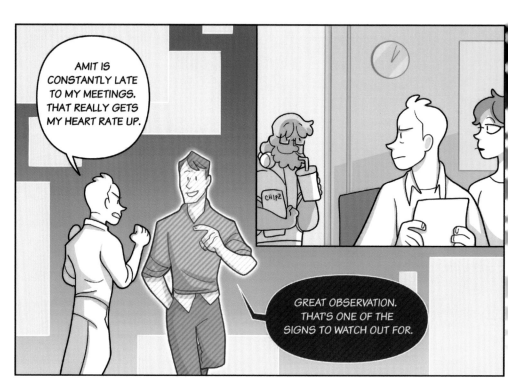

TO BE CONTINUED...

INVEST IN RELATIONSHIPS

High-performing teams are a competitive advantage that require **awareness** and **understanding** of yourself and others.

WILL-IPEDIA

Awareness is the state or ability to perceive, to feel, or to be conscious of events, objects, or sensory patterns.

Self awareness is the capacity for introspection and the ability to reconcile oneself as an individual separate from the environment and other individuals.

Team awareness is the capacity to understand the dynamics of the team and individuals that make up the team.

Social awareness is the capacity to understand how culture, group behavior, and regional and global behavior influence the individuals.

Flow is a mental or emotional state of operation when the team is fully immersed in what they are doing.

Personal triggers are external events or stimuli that evoke an instantaneous or negative emotional response.

Self Awareness

WHAT IT IS

Awareness is the state or ability to perceive, to feel, or to be conscious of events, objects, or sensory patterns. Self awareness is the ability to be conscious of our thoughts, emotions, and sensations.

WHY IT'S IMPORTANT

When we are aware of our thoughts, emotions, and sensations, we have more choices for how we respond to situations we face at work—and at home.

HOW IT WILL HELP

If we are more aware of our choices, we're more likely to make better decisions and act in ways that will increase our ability to achieve results.

HOW TO USE IT

Recall a situation from the last week or two when you had an interaction with someone that fit the following criteria:

- *You felt dissatisfied with yourself or had strong feelings about the other person involved.*

- *You felt a sense of discomfort during and after.*

- *You still feel a sense of discomfort even now as you recall the experience.*

Using the table below, answer the following questions:

1. What was the situation?

2. Which emotions were you feeling the most during the situation (e.g., anger, fear, happiness, sadness)?

3. How do you feel now as you recall this situation?

Self Awareness

Situation	Emotions Felt	Current Response
A coworker dismissed my idea	Anger, frustration	Jaw is clenched while recalling the situation

Awareness of Triggers

WHAT IT IS

Triggers are behaviors that produce an instantaneously negative emotional response. Triggers are based on behaviors, not interpretations. For example, declaring that someone is being a jerk is an interpretation. Constantly interrupting another person while they are talking is a behavior.

WHY IT'S IMPORTANT

It is important to identify our triggers, understand what lies behind them, and how to regain balance when we find ourselves triggered. Without awareness of triggers, we could simultaneously damage our relationships and negatively impact the results we are trying to create.

HOW IT WILL HELP

By understanding our triggers, learning how to manage them, and regaining our balance when we are triggered, we are more likely to achieve the results we want, behave consistently with who we want to be, and make better decisions.

HOW TO USE IT

Working effectively with our triggers in mind doesn't necessarily happen overnight. It requires patience and continued awareness. Most importantly, don't act when triggered. Take time to regain balance before you respond to the situation.

Use the table below to identify your triggers and how to regain your balance after each one.

1. In the first column, make a list of your triggers.

2. In the second column, write down your feelings associated with each trigger.

3. In the third column, write down your thoughts, assumptions, and judgments about the situation and/or person that triggered you.

Awareness of Triggers

4. In the fourth column, write down how you regain balance
   when triggered.

Triggers	Emotions Felt	Thoughts/ Assumptions/ Judgments	Regain Balance
People who interrupt me	Anger, frustration	What's their problem? They are rude and inconsiderate.	Take a breath
People who claim to know everything	Anger	They are jerks and they're arrogant.	Reconnect to purpose

Source: Gass, Robert, PhD. "The Art of Leadership." Seminar.

CHAPTER 2

CHANGE I TO WE

Success in the workplace requires a change in mindset from "I" to "we." Successful leaders know that starting discussions or addressing conflicts by developing full understanding and empathy of others' points of view will serve them better than **advocating** their initial point. Developing the ability to intelligently **flex** and **facilitate** team members will strengthen the collective team.

THE BETA PROJECT COULD REALLY IMPROVE PEOPLE'S LIVES. IT COULD HELP MY MOM AND DAD AT HOME AND A LOT OF MY FRIENDS; WE JUST NEED TO MAKE A FEW STRATEGIC CHANGES.

WE'VE BEEN WORKING ON THE BETA PROJECT FOR MONTHS, BUT AFTER TALKING WITH OUR CUSTOMERS...

IT'S TIME FOR A NEW DIRECTION.

THANKS FOR INVITING ME TO THE MEETING, KIMIKO.

GLAD YOU COULD JOIN US.

WE NEED HELP FINISHING THE DESIGNS AND TESTING THE LATEST VERSION.

HEY GUYS, EVERYTHING GOOD?

BEEN IN BACK-TO-BACK MEETINGS.

KEITH, YOU MISSED EVERYTHING. WE LANDED ON A CLEAR DIRECTION AND PRIORITIZED A COUPLE OF EXPERIMENTS.

TEAM NEXT GEN IS LAUNCHING THIS WEEK, WITH *GLOWING* REVIEWS. MAYBE IT'S TIME FOR YOU GUYS TO THROW IN THE TOWEL.

THERE'S ROOM FOR BOTH PROJECTS TO BE A HIT.

NOT REALLY...

WE ARE PLANNING NEW EXPERIMENTS BASED ON MAX'S RESEARCH.

MEH. IT'S TOO LATE FOR THAT NOW.

GEE THANKS, KEITH.

MY PLEASURE, MAX. JUST STAY OUT OF THE DRIVER'S SEAT.

WE ALL KNOW FIRST TO MARKET ALWAYS WINS.

YOU GUYS ARE ON THE WRONG TRACK.

MUCH
DESIGN
SUCH
LAYOUT
WOW

THAT MAKES SENSE.
I ALWAYS THOUGHT AMIT WAS A JERK!
I THOUGHT HE WAS CHANGING THE DESIGN
REGARDLESS OF WHAT OR HOW I SAID IT.

BUT NOT NOW?

NO, I COULD HAVE INQUIRED IF HE NEEDED HELP. I WAS FOCUSED ONLY ON THE WHAT AND NOT THE HOW. I WAS BLAMING HIM FOR THE PROBLEMS.

BLAME

YOU'VE GOT IT.

THE BLAME GAME DOESN'T WORK— NEVER HAS, NEVER WILL.

I PROBABLY COULD HAVE ASKED MIGUEL IN TODAY'S MEETING TOO.

THINK OF BLAME AS A PRODUCT OF LACK OF TRUST.

YOU NEED TO BUILD TRUST THROUGH SELF AWARENESS AND AWARENESS OF THE TEAM.

WHEN YOU DON'T WORK LIKE A TEAM, GOALS SUFFER. PEOPLE BECOME PROTECTIVE, AND THINGS DON'T IMPROVE.

MOST IMPORTANTLY, WE NEED TO CHANGE **I** TO **WE**.

I GAVE AMIT THE SPECIFICATIONS. I TOLD HIM WHAT HE NEEDED TO DO.

BUT I GUESS HE AND I NEVER REALLY TALKED ABOUT THE DESIGN. I NEVER TOLD HIM WHY IT MATTERS.

DID YOU EVER ASK AMIT WHAT MATTERS TO HIM?

I, UH.

NO.

advocacy ⟷ inquiry

I GUESS I DIDN'T...

YOU DID A GREAT JOB ADVOCATING THE DESIGNS, BUT YOU DIDN'T MAKE TIME TO INQUIRE WHAT HE THOUGHT.

ADVOCATING HAS A PLACE IN GREAT TEAMS BUT NEEDS TO BE BALANCED WITH INQUIRY.

IN FACT, DEPENDING ON THE TIME AND PLACE, ADVOCACY AND INQUIRY CAN BE USED TO GREAT SUCCESS.

FOR INSTANCE, IF I SAID YOUR SANDWICH WAS GOING TO EXPLODE, I WOULDN'T ASK, "DO YOU THINK YOU MIGHT LEAVE THE BUILDING?"

I'D TELL YOU TO LEAVE NOW, EVEN IF IT IS YOUR FAVORITE ROAST BEEF.

100% ADVOCACY!

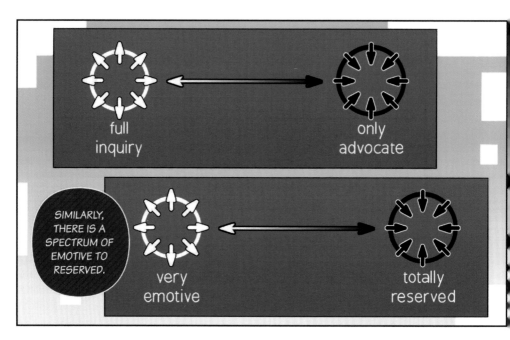

SIMILARLY, THERE IS A SPECTRUM OF EMOTIVE TO RESERVED.

full inquiry

only advocate

very emotive

totally reserved

full inquiry

BEING AWARE OF COWORKERS' PREFERENCES WILL HELP YOU TO DETERMINE HOW TO INQUIRE AND HOW YOU MIGHT HAVE THE CONVERSATION.

TRY TO FIGURE OUT THE PERSON BY THEIR BODY LANGUAGE, WORDS, AND PAST INTERACTIONS.

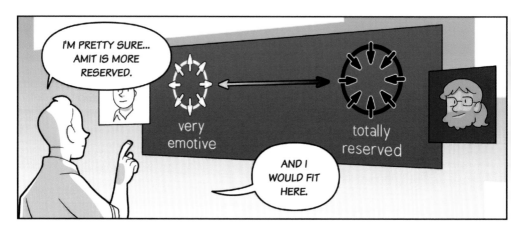

I'M PRETTY SURE... AMIT IS MORE RESERVED.

very emotive

totally reserved

AND I WOULD FIT HERE.

GREAT PRACTICE, MAX. YOU'VE LANDED ON THE IDEA OF FLEXING.

FLEXING? LIKE WITH YOGA?

SORT OF.

FLEXING IS A TEMPORARY ADJUSTMENT OF A PERSON'S BEHAVIOR TO MANAGE THE TENSION AND TO ENCOURAGE OTHERS TO ACT PRODUCTIVELY AS A TEAM.

YOU MEAN, I SHOULD BE RESERVED WHEN I'M AROUND AMIT?

YES. IF YOU WERE TO TRAVEL TO ANOTHER COUNTRY, YOU'D ADAPT (OR FLEX) TO THEIR CUSTOMS AND SOCIAL ETIQUETTE, RIGHT?

SURE, MAKES SENSE.

SO AMIT'S FROM ANOTHER COUNTRY?

METAPHORICALLY... HE IS DIFFERENT FROM YOU IN SOME WAYS, AND TO CONNECT WITH HIM, YOU CAN SOMETIMES FLEX.

I SEE.

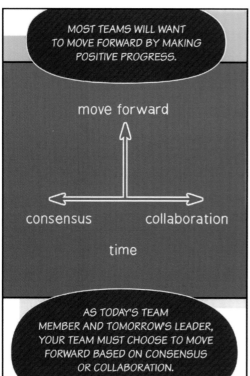

MOST TEAMS WILL WANT TO MOVE FORWARD BY MAKING POSITIVE PROGRESS.

move forward

consensus ← → collaboration

time

AS TODAY'S TEAM MEMBER AND TOMORROW'S LEADER, YOUR TEAM MUST CHOOSE TO MOVE FORWARD BASED ON CONSENSUS OR COLLABORATION.

REMEMBER, THE KEY TO MOVING FORWARD IS BALANCING ADVOCACY AND INQUIRY WHILE FLEXING.

HIGH-PERFORMING TEAMS WILL MOVE FORWARD NATURALLY.

I'M AMPED.

ME TOO, MAX!

I'LL CATCH YOU LATER!

WOW, SO MUCH TO PRACTICE... TRIGGERS, AWARENESS, FLEXING...

YIKES, ONLY 2 MINUTES UNTIL MY NEXT MEETING!

JODIE'S NOT GONNA BELIEVE THIS!

TO BE CONTINUED...

CHANGE I TO WE

Successful leaders know that high-performing teams find the right balance between delivering the **what** (tasks) and nurturing the **how** (relationships). One great strategy is leading with inquiry instead of advocacy.

What is the product or deliverable.

A **task** is the achievement of delivering the product, finishing the job.

How is the process in which you create the product. It's the conversations, the relationships, and the unspoken dialogue.

A **relationship** is how people experience engagement with each other, how people feel about their participation and contribution, and how people relate to the organization.

Advocacy is when a person publicly supports or recommends a particular point of view or preferred direction.

Inquiry is when a person asks for information from others with the intention of learning other points of view.

Flexing is a temporary adjustment of a person's behavior to manage any potential tension and to encourage others to act more productively as a team.

Boomerang

WHAT IT IS

The boomerang is a facilitation tool designed to effectively deal with conflicts or challenges that arise when you are leading, facilitating, or participating in groups.

WHY IT'S IMPORTANT

The boomerang enables you to deal with conflict and challenges by addressing the behavior in a constructive way that engages the person or group and keeps them focused.

HOW IT WILL HELP

Turning a question or challenge presented to the facilitator back to the individual or group, so as to avoid becoming defensive or argumentative, is an efficient way to keep meetings moving forward in a productive manner.

HOW TO USE IT

When confronted with a difficult person or group, or when conflict erupts in a meeting, consider the following steps.

1. Start by asking the person or people involved to share the interests or needs driving their statements. Ask what is important to them and why.

   Example: "So, John, it sounds like you don't like the direction the conversation is going. Help me understand what concerns you have and what you want."

2. Turn to the whole group and ask them what they think of the shared perspective.

   Example: "Okay, you've heard John's perspective, and he thinks we are taking too much time discussing the issue when we need a decision. How do others see it? What do others think of this situation?"

Source: Doyle, Michael, and David Straus. *How to Make Meetings Work!: The New Interaction Method.* New York: Berkley Books, 1993.

Boomerang

3. Depending on what the group says, either turn back to the original person or people involved and check for agreement or make a new process suggestion.

   Example: "Group, it looks like we all think we are spending too much time discussing this issue. Can we agree we'll only take X amount of time per issue moving forward?"

Emotion- & Action-Oriented Flexing

WHAT IT IS

Styles are predictable patterns of actions that others can observe and agree upon for describing a person's behavior.

Flexing is the adjustment of one's behavior to manage the differences in styles that exist between people.

WHY IT'S IMPORTANT

Without awareness and understanding, style differences can unintentionally result in miscommunication, frustration, or conflict.

HOW IT WILL HELP

When styles are managed well, others are encouraged to act more productively. By flexing to another person, you create space for styles to interact constructively rather than destructively.

HOW TO USE IT

There are two methods of flexing to another person: emotion-oriented and action-oriented. When observing or listening to others, pay attention to the following body, voice, and word cues to determine how both methods may be applied to reduce any tension that can result from style differences.

Emotion-Oriented Flexing

Emotion-oriented flexing requires you to be aware of whether someone is either more emotive or less emotive. In the table below, cues to the

Emotion- & Action-Oriented Flexing

left of the line indicate the person is more emotive, while cues to the right of the line indicate the person is less emotive. At the beginning of an interaction, first determine whether cues from the other person are to the left or right of the line, then match your behavior to theirs.

Body		Voice		Words	
more flowing gestures	fewer flowing gestures	more inflection	less inflection	more people-oriented	more task-oriented
more animated face	less animated face	more varied pace	more even pace	more feeling-oriented	more fact-oriented
free body movement	controlled body movement				

Action-Oriented Flexing

Action-oriented flexing requires you to be aware of whether someone prefers to take action by telling more (advocating) or asking more (inquiry). In the table below, cues to the right of the line indicate the person prefers telling more and cues to the left of the line indicate the person prefers asking more.

Body		Voice		Words	
leans backward	leans forward	speaks more softly	speaks more loudly	expresses opinions less strongly	expresses opinions more strongly
slower pace	faster pace	speaks with less intensity	speaks with more intensity	asks	tells
less directive gestures	more directive gestures	speaks more slowly	speaks more rapidly		
less direct eye contact	more direct eye contact				

Balancing Inquiry & Advocacy

WHAT IT IS

Inquiry means listening and asking good questions to deepen your understanding of another person's point of view before responding with your own.

Advocacy means stating your point of view. Use *skillful* advocacy, which requires you to share your reasoning. *Positional* advocacy, on the other hand, is sharing your view as if it is a finished product without revealing your reasoning, thus preventing others from understanding your data, logic, or concerns.

WHY IT'S IMPORTANT

When engaged in challenging conversations, rather than just declaring your point of view, use inquiry and advocacy to deepen your understanding of the other person's perspective. A lack of inquiry or advocacy can lead to defensiveness and exacerbate the situation.

HOW IT WILL HELP

Balancing inquiry and advocacy leads to a more productive conversation.

HOW TO USE IT

To prepare for a difficult conversation, consider the following steps.

1. Review the following example questions and prioritize which ones might help you.

    - *"Will you help me understand how you see things?"*

    - *"Why is this important to you? What are your key interests and concerns?"*

    - *"What do you need here? What are your priorities?"*

Balancing Inquiry & Advocacy

- *"What experiences have you had that inform your perspective?"*

- *"What am I missing?"*

2. During the difficult conversation, ask the questions you prioritized in step 1 before offering your perspective, especially if the issue being discussed is contentious.

3. When you do share your perspective, use skillful advocacy instead of positional advocacy. Skillful advocacy examples include:

- *"Here is what is most important to me..."*

- *"Let me share with you my concerns and my thinking behind them."*

- *"This is my working assumption about that situation."*

CHAPTER 3

SHIFT CONFUSION TO CLARITY

We've all felt the side effects of confusion, frustration, poor performance, mistakes, and even avoidable failure. That's why it's so important to shift from confusion to clarity. High-performing teams rely on clear communication (using tools like **mirroring**), practice **mindfulness**, and clearly define the team's **goals** and individual **roles**.

I DIDN'T THINK ANYONE IN THIS COMPANY REALLY UNDERSTOOD ME... AMIT, MIGUEL, AND THE REST OF THE TEAM...

BUT NOW MAYBE I CAN CHANGE.

MAYBE WILL WAS RIGHT!

HEY KIARA, HOW WAS YOUR WEEKEND?

GOOD. WHAT'S UP?

AS YOU KNOW, I'VE BEEN WORKING ON THE BETA PRODUCT. OUR COMPANY IS BIG ON INNOVATION AND OUR TEAM BRAINSTORMED A BRAND NEW DIRECTION FOR THE PRODUCT.

I'VE SHARED THE RESEARCH WITH THE TEAM AND WE ALL WANT TO EXPERIMENT FURTHER.

OK, I'D NEED TO LOOK AT THE RESEARCH IN THE FUTURE.

GREAT. MAYBE SOMETIME THIS WEEK?

80

SPEAKING OF INQUIRY, A GREAT TOOL IS **MIRRORING**.

EVERYONE WANTS TO BE HEARD, BUT THE KEY TO GREAT LISTENING IS TO REALLY UNDERSTAND WHAT'S BEING SAID.

MIRRORING IS ACTIVELY LISTENING TO THE PERSON IN A ONE-ON-ONE MEETING, OR EVEN BETTER, IN A GROUP MEETING.

JUST REFLECT WHAT YOU HEARD AND GIVE IT A TRY.

SO, WHAT DID I JUST SAY?

THE KEY TO LISTENING IS TO UNDERSTAND WHAT'S BEING SAID.

YOU CAN GET REALLY GOOD AT MIRRORING BECAUSE YOU CAN LISTEN AND SHARE BACK WHAT YOU HEARD,

BUT YOU CAN ALSO MIRROR A PERSON'S EMOTIONAL STATE BASED ON VISUAL CUES.

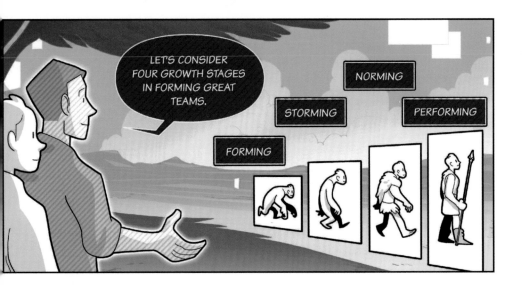

LET'S CONSIDER FOUR GROWTH STAGES IN FORMING GREAT TEAMS.

FORMING

STORMING

NORMING

PERFORMING

LET'S START WITH FORMING.

FORMING IS THE SETUP STAGE WHERE THE TEAM IS ASSEMBLED.

TEAM MEMBERS COME TOGETHER. THEY MAY NOT HAVE A HISTORY WORKING TOGETHER, OR PERHAPS NO REAL WORK EXPERIENCE.

TYPICALLY, IN THE FORMING STAGE THE TEAM'S MOTIVATION IS HIGH AND THE PERFORMANCE IS SLOW.

SOMETIMES THE FORMING STAGE COULD BE CONSIDERED THE HONEYMOON STAGE; EVERYONE'S EXCITED TO JOIN A NEW PROJECT BUT STILL NEEDS TO FIGURE OUT HOW TO MOVE FORWARD.

IN MY CASE... SOMETIMES NOT.

NOT EVERYONE IS ASKED TO FORM A TEAM UNDER IDEAL CONDITIONS.

STORMING IS THE NEXT STAGE WHERE THE TEAM STARTS WORKING TOGETHER.

JUST LIKE A STORM, DRAMATIC CONFLICTS CAN OCCUR. TEAM MEMBERS WILL START TO COLLIDE, WHICH CAN RESULT IN SOME EXPLOSIVE BEHAVIOR.

IT'S USUALLY THE TEAM THAT LACKS TOOLS, CLEAR ROLES, AND SHARED GOALS.

LEVERAGING OUR BEST PRACTICES OF AWARENESS, INQUIRY. AND TECHNIQUES LIKE THE BOOMERANG WILL HELP.

IN THE STORMING STAGE, MOTIVATION DROPS AS TEAM MEMBERS LOSE FOCUS, AND PERFORMANCE IS LOW.

WOW, THAT'S DEPRESSING.

A COMMON GOAL IS THE FOUNDATION FOR ANY TEAM. A GOAL BRINGS TOGETHER UNITY OF PURPOSE RATHER THAN INDIVIDUAL GOALS.

A GREAT GOAL GIVES DIRECTION TO A TEAM, IDENTIFIES WHERE THEY ARE NOW...

...AND WHERE THE TEAM WANTS TO GO.

SHOW OFF!

MORE IMPORTANTLY, A COMMON GOAL WILL CREATE A SENSE OF IDENTITY.

WITHOUT A SHARED GOAL THE TEAM WON'T HAVE DIRECTION OR UNITY.

THE TEAM WON'T EVOLVE PAST STORMING TO BECOME A GREAT PERFORMING TEAM.

WHAT MAKES A GREAT GOAL?

GOOD QUESTION, LET'S THINK ABOUT THEM AS **SMART** GOALS!

SMART GOALS?

SECONDLY, THE GOAL MUST BE **MEASURABLE**.

THE TEAM SHOULD ESTABLISH CRITERIA FOR SUCCESS. THIS WILL HELP THE TEAM TRACK PROGRESS AND GIVE AN INCENTIVE TO KEEP GOING.

A GOOD MEASUREMENT COULD BE A DATE, A DOLLAR AMOUNT, OR ANY OTHER APPROPRIATE UNIT.

LIKE GOALS IN A HOCKEY GAME!

NEXT, A GOAL SHOULD BE **ACHIEVABLE**.

YOU KNOW, SOMETHING REASONABLE AND WITHIN THE ABILITY OF THE TEAM.

THE TEAM SHOULD ALL AGREE WHAT'S ACHIEVABLE. AN OVERLY DIFFICULT GOAL WILL BREAK THE FLOW AND MORE THAN LIKELY LEAD TO FAILURE.

SOMETHING EASY?

WELL, A GREAT GOAL MAY BE A STRETCH FOR THE TEAM, BUT IT SHOULDN'T BE EXTREME.

A GOAL SHOULD BE **RELEVANT**. IDENTIFY GOALS THAT ARE IMPORTANT TO YOU AND THE TEAM. THE TEAM WILL START LEVERAGING THEIR EXPERTISE TO MAKE THE GOAL COME TRUE.

WHEN GOALS AREN'T RELEVANT, WELL, TYPICALLY THE TEAM LOSES MOTIVATION PRETTY QUICKLY.

THAT'S SILLY.

YES, BUT YOU'D BE SURPRISED HOW MANY SET GOALS ARE NOT EVEN RELEVANT.

CLEAR MILESTONES, DEADLINES, AND AN AGREEMENT BY ALL TEAM MEMBERS MAKE GOALS **TIME-BOUND,** THE LAST COMPONENT OF A SMART GOAL.

TIME

00:30

TIME-BOUND GOALS CREATE A SENSE OF URGENCY AND PREVENT THE TEAM FROM LOSING FOCUS.

WHEN TEAM MEMBERS **ACCEPT, UNDERSTAND,** AND **COMMIT** TO DELIVER ON A SMART GOAL...

...YOU KNOW YOU'LL BE ABLE TO ACHIEVE GREAT THINGS!

NICE GAME, WILL!

SMART GOALS MAKE A LOT OF SENSE!

YES, BUT GOALS ARE ONLY HALF THE EQUATION.

LET'S TALK ABOUT THE FINAL PIECE OF A TEAM: THE TEAM MEMBERS' **ROLES**.

ONE OF THE BIGGEST PROBLEMS WITH TEAMS IS DISCUSSING ROLE CLARITY.

I'VE EXPERIENCED THIS BEFORE... AND I'M UNSURE ABOUT THE DISTINCTION BETWEEN KEITH'S ROLE AND MINE ON OUR NEW PROJECT.

COACH

TO ENABLE A HIGH-PERFORMING TEAM, EACH TEAM MEMBER SHOULD HAVE A CLEAR PICTURE OF EVERY TEAM MEMBER'S ROLE.

REF

IT WOULD BE STRANGE IF THE GOALIE SUDDENLY STARTED COACHING, OR IF COACH BEGAN TO DEFEND THE NET.

COACH

TEAM MEMBERS SHOULD KNOW WHO IS DOING WHAT TASK AND WHO IS RESPONSIBLE FOR WHAT.

AND TEAM MEMBERS SHOULD KNOW WHO HAS THE AUTHORITY TO DO WHAT.

LASTLY, LET'S TALK ABOUT **AUTHORITY**.

YIPES, THIS PART CAN GET TRICKY.

AUTHORITY IS THE LEVEL OF CAPABILITY TO MAKE DECISIONS WITHIN THE ROLE.

AUTHORITY APPLIES TO EVERYONE ON THE TEAM, IT JUST NEEDS TO BE IDENTIFIED.

THE LEVEL OF AUTHORITY ALLOWS SPACE AND FREEDOM FOR EACH TEAM MEMBER TO MAKE FINAL DECISIONS.

JUST AS THE GOALIE MAKES THE FINAL DECISION ON HOW TO DEFEND THE NET, BUT THE COACH MAKES THE FINAL DECISION ON PULLING THE GOALIE OR KEEPING HIM IN THE GAME.

OF COURSE, ANYONE IN AUTHORITY SHOULD SEEK OUT INPUT FROM THE TEAM MEMBERS.

ATTENTION ON PURPOSE, MINDFULNESS IS ABOUT CONSCIOUS DIRECTION OF OUR AWARENESS.

IT'S ABOUT LISTENING CAREFULLY TO A CONVERSATION WITH KIARA, AMIT, OR KEITH. IF OUR MIND WANDERS, IT'S ABOUT REFOCUSING AND PURPOSEFULLY PAYING ATTENTION.

I HAVE SUCH A HABIT OF THINKING ABOUT OTHER THINGS WHILE SOMEONE IS TALKING.

EVERYONE DOES, JUST PRACTICE.

THINK OF MINDFULNESS LIKE A MUSCLE. TO IMPROVE, YOU NEED TO EXERCISE YOUR MINDFULNESS MUSCLE EVERY DAY.

NEXT, ATTENTION IN THE PRESENT MOMENT: IT'S EASY TO THINK ABOUT THE PAST OR THINGS THAT MAY HAPPEN IN THE FUTURE, BUT MINDFULNESS IS ABOUT FOCUSING ON THE PRESENT MOMENT.

LIKE WHEN MY MIND WANDERS AND STARTS THINKING ABOUT THE NEXT MEETING OR A MEETING THAT JUST HAPPENED.

IT'S EASY TO GET UNFOCUSED. BUT HONOR THE CURRENT MEETING OR REQUEST A RESCHEDULE.

FINALLY, BEING NONJUDGMENTAL: MINDFULNESS IS ABOUT ACCEPTANCE.

PAYING ATTENTION TO OUR THOUGHTS AND FEELINGS WITHOUT JUDGMENT.

IF THE CONFLICT TRULY IMPACTS THE GOAL, PUT IT ON A SCALE OF ONE TO FIVE.

IF THE CONFLICT DOESN'T IMPACT THE GOAL, IT'S A SCALE OF ONE. THIS IS THE PRACTICE OF STRATEGIC ACCEPTANCE.

DON'T MISUNDERSTAND, YOU SURFACE CONFLICT WITH YOUR TEAM, BUT SET THE CONTEXT OF IMPACT.

REMEMBER, NOT EVERYONE WILL SHARE THE SAME CONCERN.

BUT AT LEAST YOU CAN THEN INQUIRE WHY AND BOOMERANG ANY RECOMMENDATIONS TO THE TEAM.

FINALLY, LET'S TALK ABOUT SOME MINDFULNESS TIPS.

MOST PEOPLE MOVE AT A VERY QUICK PACE DURING THE DAY, SO START EACH DAY WITH A FEW MINUTES OF PERSONAL AWARENESS.

FIND SOME TIME DURING THE DAY FOR SELF-REFLECTION. DO THIS WITHOUT JUDGMENT.

END EACH DAY WITH AWARENESS OF YOUR ACCOMPLISHMENTS, NEEDS, AND DIFFICULTIES, AND THOSE OF OTHERS.

THANKS, WILL.

IT'S HARD TO PUT THINGS IN PERSPECTIVE SOMETIMES. YOU ARE RIGHT; NOT EVERYTHING IS A CATASTROPHIC BATTLE.

ABSOLUTELY, IT'S NEVER A BATTLE WHEN YOU FIND A BALANCE BETWEEN FOCUSING ON THE WHAT AND THE HOW.

TO BE CONTINUED...

SHIFT CONFUSION TO CLARITY

Awareness of the **four stages of growth** for teams can help leadership provide support and guidance to navigate the changes. Successful leaders will help the team get clarity on shared **goals** and individual **roles** within the team.

Mirroring means actively listening to a person in a 1:1 meeting or in a group meeting.

Four growth stages for great teams: Forming, Storming, Norming, and Performing.

Forming describes when the team is first assembled.

Storming describes when the team starts working together and any conflict is addressed.

Norming occurs when the team learns how to work together.

Performing describes when the team is at peak performance and motivation is high.

A **goal** provides a core mission for the team. **SMART goals** are specific, measurable, achievable, relevant, and time-bound.

Roles help team members understand who is responsible for certain tasks and who has authority to make certain decisions.

Mindfulness means paying attention in particular ways: on purpose, in the present moment, and without judgment.

Listening & Asking Questions

WHAT IT IS

Listening and asking good questions is what inquiry is all about.

WHY IT'S IMPORTANT

All too often, we are rehearsing our response to the other person while they are answering our questions. We tend to agree or disagree without fully understanding the other person's perspective.

HOW IT WILL HELP

Inquiry deepens our understanding of another person's perspective before sharing our own.

HOW TO USE IT

Find a partner and decide who will be the **questioner** and who will be the **speaker**. For the purpose of this exercise, the questioner may only ask questions based on the speaker's answers.

1. *Speaker:* Begin by introducing yourself. Include your name and job title.

2. *Questioner:* Respond by asking one open-ended question that demonstrates your genuine curiosity about the speaker's job responsibilities, current opportunities, or work challenges.

3. *Speaker:* Answer the question thoroughly.

4. *Questioner:* The response to your first question is the key to your next question. Continue asking open-ended questions for the duration of the exercise.

5. *Speaker:* Continue answering the questions thoroughly. At the end of the exercise, provide feedback to the questioner regarding the quality of questions asked and the impact these questions had on you.

Mindfulness

WHAT IT IS

Mindfulness is the practice of bringing one's attention to the internal and external experiences happening in the present moment. It is moment-to-moment awareness without judgment.

WHY IT'S IMPORTANT

Benefits of a mindfulness practice include: stress reduction, better focus and concentration, being more open to creative ideas, greater cognitive flexibility, boosts to working memory, less emotional reactivity, and improved relationships.

HOW IT WILL HELP

Practicing mindfulness can result in greater presence, greater fulfillment, behavior change, and knowing yourself at a deeper level.

HOW TO USE IT

Choose one of the options below to **start your mindfulness practice.**

Option #1: Relax and breathe. Throughout the day, take a moment or two (between 1 and 10 minutes) and focus on relaxing your breathing. Just simply watch your breathing—in and out. Try this with your eyes closed.

Don't try to affect your breathing in any way. Let it happen naturally. Just notice. Any and all thoughts, feelings, sensations, or disturbances that may arise during this exercise are all just fine. Just notice them and come back to watching your breathing.

Option #2: With each breath, count backward from 20—breathing in, breathing out 20, breathing in, breathing out 19, breathing in, breathing out 18, etc. If you lose track of your breaths, start back at 20.

Option #3: Find a favorite piece of music that is relaxing. Simply listen to the music while relaxing your breathing. See all thoughts, emotions, and sensations as clouds passing in the sky.

Mindfulness

Choose one of the options below to **end your mindfulness practice.**

Option #1: Take a moment and imagine the rest of your day, especially if you started the day with this practice. What are your goals for the day? What are your top three priorities? How do you want to feel throughout the day? Visualize a great day.

Option #2: Read an inspirational quote, prayer, or saying to serve as an anchor that will remind you of this practice throughout the day.

CHAPTER 4

DRIVE FOR YES

High-performing teams deliver results by positively handling **how** they approach the work and **what** they are trying to achieve. Getting to great results requires a culture of **yes**. In a culture of yes, a team is aligned toward a single vision and takes collaborative steps to get there. Leveraging tools like **escalation** and the **ladder of inference** will be necessary in the course of any project.

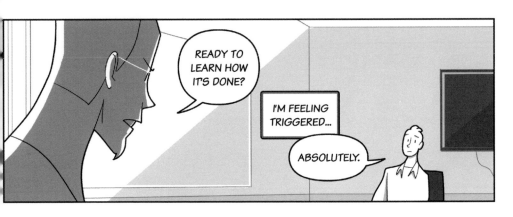

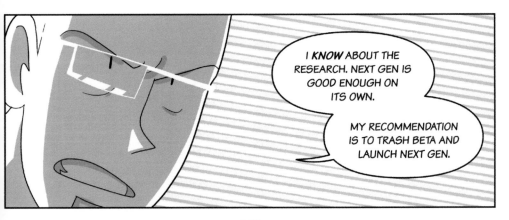

118

LET'S TALK ABOUT DEALING WITH DIFFICULT PEOPLE AND TWO OPTIONS TO CONSIDER: **THE LADDER OF INFERENCE** AND, IF THAT DOESN'T WORK, **ESCALATION.**

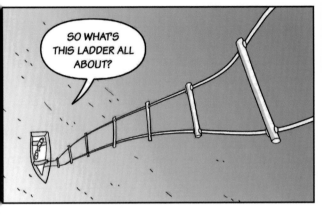

SO WHAT'S THIS LADDER ALL ABOUT?

EVERY TIME WE INTERACT WITH SOMEONE, WE EXPERIENCE A METAPHORICAL LADDER. WE CLIMB THE LADDER IN MILLISECONDS. WE START AT THE BOTTOM, CLIMB EACH RUNG, AND EXIT AT THE TOP.

EACH RUNG IS A SEPARATE STEP THAT IMPACTS HOW WE MAKE CHOICES AND TAKE ACTION.

AND INFERENCE MEANS A CONCLUSION REACHED ON THE BASIS OF SOLID REASONING.

THAT'S RIGHT. LET'S DISCUSS THE SOLIDITY OF THAT REASONING.

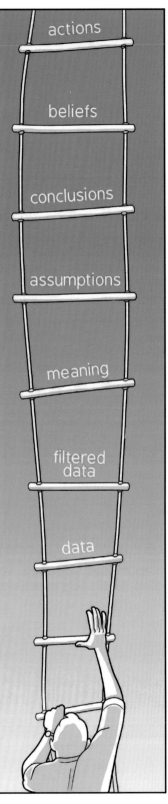

actions

beliefs

conclusions

assumptions

meaning

filtered data

data

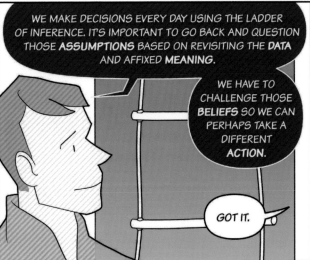

LET'S THINK ABOUT SOMETHING THAT EVERYBODY CAN RELATE TO—THE WAY OUR INFERENCE RELATES TO **TIME.**

WE ONLY HAVE SO MUCH TIME AND IT CAN BE CHALLENGING TO MANAGE.

THE LADDER OF INFERENCE NOT ONLY APPLIES TO COWORKERS, IT ALSO APPLIES TO YOU WHEN YOU FILTER DATA AND MAKE ASSUMPTIONS. IT CAN LEAD TO INAPPROPRIATE ACTIONS JUST LIKE BEING TRIGGERED.

WHEN DO WE EXPECT THINGS TO BE DONE? WHERE SHOULD WE SPEND OUR TIME? WHAT SHOULD WE BE SPENDING OUR TIME ON? HOW CAN WE BEST MAXIMIZE OUR TIME?

WE KNOW THAT EVERYONE MANAGES TIME DIFFERENTLY WHILE UNDER PRESSURE, SO WE CAN PREDICT THAT STORMING MAY OCCUR AND THAT PEOPLE MAY BE TRIGGERED.

IT'S IMPORTANT TO BE AWARE OF YOUR RELATIONSHIP TO TIME AND THE WAY IN WHICH OTHERS RELATE TO TIME AS IT CAN OFTEN TRIGGER SOMETHING IN YOU.

JUST LIKE THAT COWORKER TEXTING IN THE MEETING. THERE WAS AN ASSUMPTION HE WASN'T PAYING ATTENTION AND WAS WASTING TIME.

IT'S CLEAR ONE PERSON'S ACTIONS CAN REALLY IMPACT OTHERS.

LET'S SEE HOW POSITIVE AND NEGATIVE ACTIONS RELATED TO TIME CAN REALLY IMPACT OTHERS.

HAVE YOU EVER...

ACCEPTED AND ATTENDED A MEETING BUT ARE THINKING ABOUT THE NEXT MEETING OR A PREVIOUS MEETING? DOES THAT HONOR YOUR COMMITMENT TO THE TEAM?

YOU KNOW, IF YOU CAN'T SHOW UP AND BE PRESENT, THEN SHARE YOUR MINDSET WITH THE TEAM. ASK FOR THE BEST WAY TO MOVE FORWARD.

DELIVERED IMPORTANT INFORMATION, BUT RUSHED OFF IMMEDIATELY AFTERWARDS? HOW DOES THAT IMPACT THE RECEIVER?

YOU COULD CONSIDER WAITING FOR FEEDBACK OR SUGGESTING A TIME TO FOLLOW UP.

SCHEDULED A PRESENTATION LOOKING FOR FEEDBACK BUT DIDN'T ALLOCATE ENOUGH TIME FOR DISCUSSION? WHAT SIGNAL DOES THAT SEND?

TRY CREATING AN AGENDA TO ENSURE TIME FOR FEEDBACK, SENDING THE PRESENTATION IN ADVANCE, OR SCHEDULING A FOLLOWUP MEETING FOR FEEDBACK.

MISSED A DEADLINE FOR REASONABLE REASONS BUT FORGOT TO INFORM OTHERS? HOW DOES THIS AFFECT THE TEAM AND THE TRUST?

CANCELLED A MEETING AT THE LAST MINUTE SINCE YOU WERE DOUBLE-BOOKED? HOW DID THIS LAST MINUTE CANCELLATION IMPACT OTHERS?

EVERYONE MISSES DEADLINES, BUT IT'S ABOUT ANTICIPATING MISSING THE DEADLINE AND CREATING CLARITY BEFORE THE LAST MINUTE.

IT'S ABOUT ANTICIPATION. CHECK YOUR CALENDAR THE DAY BEFORE TO AVOID DOUBLE-BOOKED MEETINGS. OR EVEN BETTER, DON'T DOUBLE-BOOK MEETINGS. SAY YES, JUST NOT AT THIS TIME.

ARRIVED LATE FOR A MEETING THAT REQUIRES EVERYONE TO PAUSE AND CATCH YOU UP?

HOW DOES THAT IMPACT PRODUCTIVITY?

IT'S EASY TO BE LATE FOR A MEETING, SO JUST ASK WHAT'S BEST FOR THE TEAM: STOP AND REPEAT OR CONTINUE TO MOVE FORWARD?

ATTENDED A MEETING AND DOMINATED THE CONVERSATION? FAILED TO MAKE TIME FOR OTHERS TO SHARE THEIR PERSPECTIVE?

I'D BE SURPRISED IF MOST PEOPLE HAVEN'T DONE OR EXPERIENCED MOST OF THESE EXAMPLES.

THAT'S REASONABLE. THE CHALLENGE HERE IS BEING AWARE, BEING MINDFUL, AND TAKING PREEMPTIVE ACTION TO KEEP THE TEAM FLOW GOING.

IT'S ABOUT SELF AWARENESS AND TEAM AWARENESS. JUST REMEMBER, SOMETIMES IT'S BEST TO TAKE A PAUSE.

127

SO, LET'S CHAT ABOUT KEITH.

I'VE OBSERVED YOUR INTERACTIONS WITH HIM THROUGHOUT THE DAY.

EVEN WITH ALL THE BEST PRACTICES OF AWARENESS, TRIGGERS, AND MINDFULNESS, DIFFICULT SITUATIONS AND BAD BEHAVIOR WILL HAPPEN.

THEY CAN OCCUR IN ONE-ON-ONE MEETINGS OR GROUP MEETINGS.

WHAT DO YOU MEAN BY BAD BEHAVIOR?

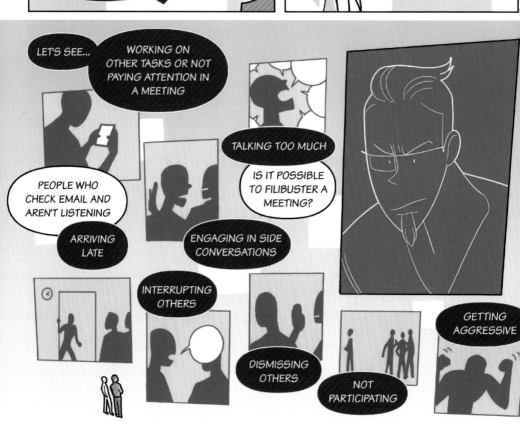

LET'S SEE...

WORKING ON OTHER TASKS OR NOT PAYING ATTENTION IN A MEETING

TALKING TOO MUCH

IS IT POSSIBLE TO FILIBUSTER A MEETING?

PEOPLE WHO CHECK EMAIL AND AREN'T LISTENING

ARRIVING LATE

ENGAGING IN SIDE CONVERSATIONS

INTERRUPTING OTHERS

DISMISSING OTHERS

NOT PARTICIPATING

GETTING AGGRESSIVE

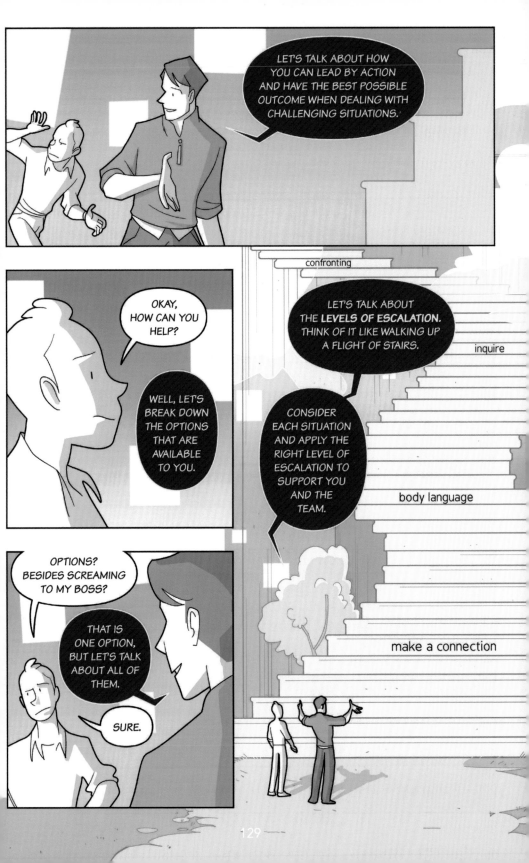

130

THAT COULD BE A LITTLE AWKWARD.

IT COULD BE. NINETY-NINE PERCENT OF CONFLICT BETWEEN PEOPLE CAN BE RESOLVED BEFORE IT NEEDS TO BE SHARED WITH THE LARGER GROUP.

MOST ISSUES CAN BE RESOLVED WITH A PERSONAL CONNECTION, A BIT OF INQUIRY, AND A ONE-ON-ONE CONVERSATION.

THAT'S GOOD.

NEVER AVOID THE SITUATION. TAKE TIME TO FIGURE OUT WHAT'S GOING ON.

YEAH, THAT MAKES SENSE.

AND THESE CONVERSATIONS ARE THE PERFECT TIME TO SHARE YOUR EXPERIENCE DURING MOMENTS OF CONFLICT.

133

134

LET'S START WITH DATA. WHAT'S HAPPENED SO FAR?

LEADERSHIP HAS ASKED ME TO MERGE PRODUCTS, NEXT GEN IS ABOUT TO LAUNCH, AND BETA HAS UNCOVERED NEW RESEARCH FINDINGS.

AND KEITH?

WELL, HE DOESN'T WANT TO MERGE PROJECTS AND HAS DISMISSED THE RESEARCH.

AND...

AND WE BOTH HAVE BEEN WORKING ON SEPARATE BUT SIMILAR PROJECTS FOR A YEAR.

HOW DOES KEITH ACT?

HE IS PASSIONATE AND DEFENSIVE. HE WANTS TO LAUNCH NEXT GEN.

WHAT ABOUT KEITH'S BACKGROUND?

HE HAS BEEN AT THE COMPANY A LONG TIME AND JOINED VIA AN ACQUISITION.

WHAT ELSE IS THERE?

INQUIRE.

135

HELLO? DID YOU HIT YOUR HEAD?

UM...

I KNOW WE ONLY HAVE 10 MINUTES, BUT WE DON'T KNOW EACH OTHER THAT WELL.

SO HOW DID YOU GET STARTED IN NEXT GEN?

I STARTED ABOUT THREE YEARS AGO. WAY BEFORE YOU EVEN STARTED AT THE COMPANY. THAT ORIGINAL PROJECT WAS CALLED ALPHA.

I HEARD YOU JOINED THE COMPANY VIA AN ACQUISITION.

MY COMPANY WAS ACQUIRED ABOUT TWO YEARS AGO.

WERE YOU EXCITED ABOUT BEING ACQUIRED?

YES, SINCE I COULD CONTINUE THE RESEARCH AND WORK ON ALPHA.

IT'S GREAT THAT THE COMPANY WAS SUPPORTIVE.

NOT REALLY. IT WAS A PRETTY CUTTHROAT CULTURE. SOMETHING *YOU* COULDN'T HANDLE.

I SPENT ALMOST A YEAR WORKING WITH LEADERSHIP TO CHANGE THE DIRECTION OF THE PROJECT. BUT THE PROPOSAL WAS TRASHED AFTER A YEAR OF HARD WORK.

AND WE WEREN'T REWARDED FOR TRASHED PROJECTS.

WE WERE ACQUIRED AND NEXT GEN WAS BORN.

THAT MUST HAVE BEEN BRUTAL.

AT THE TIME, I WAS TOLD IT WAS A WASTE OF TIME. I JUST DIDN'T HAVE THE SUPPORT.

I DON'T WANT TO HAVE THAT HAPPEN AGAIN.

I'M NOT 100% HAPPY WITH NEXT GEN, BUT THE SHIP IS ABOUT TO SAIL.

THAT EXPLAINS KEITH'S BEHAVIOR. HE WANTS THE PROJECT TO SUCCEED, HE BELIEVED IN THE RESEARCH, BUT DOESN'T WANT TO RISK IT AGAIN.

GOOD CONCLUSION. WHAT ARE YOUR BELIEFS NOW?

KEITH AND I BOTH BELIEVE IN THE RESEARCH.

WE BOTH WANT TO MAKE GREAT PRODUCTS.

WE BOTH WANT TO SUCCEED.

I CAN APPRECIATE THAT, BUT IT WOULD BE AWFUL TO SEE ALL YOUR ORIGINAL IDEAS GO TO WASTE.

THAT'S TRUE.

KIARA WOULD BE SUPPORTIVE. JUST LIKE YOU... OUR COMPANY WANTS TO SHIP BECAUSE THE TEAM IS CONFIDENT AND EXCITED ABOUT THE SOLUTION, NOT BECAUSE OF A DEADLINE.

I GUESS MAYBE LEADERSHIP WOULD BE SUPPORTIVE NOW. EVEN YOU MIGHT BE HELPFUL. CAN YOU TALK TO KIARA ABOUT IT?

ABSOLUTELY. I'D BE HAPPY TO VOLUNTEER.

EXCELLENT.

WOW, WE'VE BEEN TALKING FOR THIRTY MINUTES. I'M SO LATE!

LET'S TALK MORE TOMORROW.

THANKS, KEITH.

THANKS, MAX.

TO BE CONTINUED...

DRIVE FOR YES

Difficult conversations will inevitably occur in any organization. To create space for thoughtful decision making requires awareness and an understanding of the thinking process. With tools like **escalation** and the **ladder of inference**, leaders and teams will be equipped to make more informed decisions.

WILL-IPEDIA

Ladder of inference describes the thinking process that we go through, usually without realizing it, to get from a fact to a decision or action.

The ladder of inference has seven steps: data, filtered data, meaning, assumptions, conclusions, beliefs, and actions.

Pausing refers to taking a break for reflection and being mindful of what's happening in the moment.

Escalation refers to the different levels involved when dealing with potential challenges in a variety of contexts. The levels of escalation include making a connection, using body language, leading with inquiry, and confrontation.

Ladder of Inference

WHAT IT IS

The ladder of inference describes the thought process that we may go through, usually without realizing it, to get from a fact to a decision or action. The stages of thought can be seen as rungs on a ladder, starting with observable data on the lowest rung to our multiple interpretations of the data on the upper rungs.

Observable data is the filtered data we choose to focus on, the meaning and assumptions we add to it, the conclusions we make, the beliefs we build, and the actions we decide to take.

WHY IT'S IMPORTANT

We often leap up the ladder, going from data to our conclusions and then action so quickly that we often act as if our conclusions are, in fact, data.

By allowing others to explore our thinking (the gaps between data and action) and by exploring the thinking of others, we arrive at more effective solutions.

HOW IT WILL HELP

Intentionally going through each step of the thought process, or climbing each rung of the ladder of inference, empowers us to make more informed and effective decisions.

HOW TO USE IT

Share your thought process with others (i.e., climb up your ladder of inference), and ask questions to understand someone else's thought process (i.e., help them climb up their ladder of inference). Keep these tips in mind:

- *When engaged in a difficult conversation, it is important to minimize leaping to assumptions or conclusions. Don't skip rungs on the ladder of inference.*

Ladder of Inference

- *When sharing your point of view, let the listener(s) know the data you are relying on, the meaning you are adding, the conclusions you are making, the beliefs you are building, and the actions you will take.*

- *When others are sharing their view, ask questions to better understand the data they are observing, the meaning they are adding, the conclusions they are making, the beliefs they are building, and the actions they will take.*

Source: Senge, Peter M. The Fifth Discipline Fieldbook: Strategies and Tools for Building a Learning Organization. New York: Doubleday, 1994.

CHAPTER 5

FEEL THE DIFFERENCE

With enough practice, you'll be able to start applying the tools and techniques to support high-performing teams and grow as a leader. You'll establish a habit of **facilitation** and **collaboration**, and you will move from seeing the difference to feeling the difference. You'll be able to identify areas of concern and make suggestions to correct challenging situations.

THIS HAS BEEN THE LONGEST DAY OF MY LIFE. I CAN'T BELIEVE EVERYTHING THAT'S HAPPENED.

I CAN'T WAIT TO TELL JODIE AND KIARA ABOUT MY MEETING WITH KEITH.

KEITH AND I HAVE A LOT IN COMMON.

I FEEL EMPOWERED AND READY TO TACKLE THE MERGER AS A TEAM.

I'M GOING TO FOCUS ON THE WHAT AND THE HOW.

I'LL SET UP A ONE-ON-ONE WITH AMIT FOR TOMORROW.

PLUS, MIGUEL AND KIMIKO ALREADY SET UP A MEETING TO DISCUSS NEXT STEPS. I'LL SHARE THE NEWS ABOUT KEITH.

AND KEITH AND I CAN START WORKING TOGETHER ON THE MERGER.

KIARA WILL BE HAPPY AND WAY LESS STRESSED.

YOU KNOW, I THINK THIS JOB IS GOING TO WORK OUT.

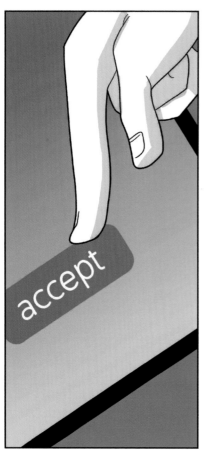

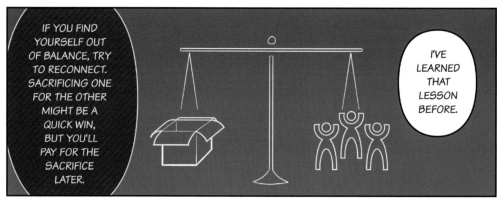

152

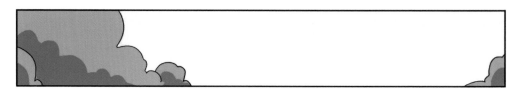

BIBLIOGRAPHY

CHAPTER 1: INVEST IN RELATIONSHIPS

Csikszentmihalyi, Mihaly. **Finding Flow: The Psychology of Engagement with Everyday Life (Masterminds Series)**. New York, NY: Basic Books, 1998.

Gass, Robert, PhD. **The Art of Leadership.** Seminar.

Goleman, Daniel. **Working with Emotional Intelligence**. New York, NY: Bantam Books, 1998.

Goleman, Daniel. **The Executive Edge: An Insider's Guide to Outstanding Leadership**. Northampton, MA: More Than Sound, 2015.

Stone, Douglas, Sheila Heen, and Bruce Patton. **Difficult Conversations: How to Discuss What Matters Most**. London: Penguin, 2010.

CHAPTER 2: CHANGE I TO WE

Gunnlaugson, Olen, and Michael Brabant. **Cohering the Integral We Space: Engaging Collective Emergence, Wisdom and Healing in Groups**. Albany, NY: Integral Publishing House, 2016.

Elgin, Suzette Haden. **How to Disagree Without Being Disagreeable: Getting Your Point Across with the Gentle Art of Verbal Self-Defense**. New York: John Wiley & Sons, 1997.

Kofman, Fred. **Conscious Business: How to Build Value Through Value**. Boulder, CO: Sounds True, 2013.

Kramlinger, Thomas, and Larry Wilson. **The Social Styles Handbook: Adapt Your Style to Win Trust**. Belgium: Nova Vista, 2011.

Senge, Peter. **The Fifth Discipline: The Art & Practice of the Learning Organization**. New York, NY: Random House Business, 2006.

Doyle, Michael, and David Straus. **How to Make Meetings Work!: The New Interaction Method**. New York, NY: Berkley Books, 1993.

CHAPTER 3: SHIFT CONFUSION TO CLARITY

Egolf, Donald B., and Sondra L. Chester. **Forming, Storming, Norming, Performing: Successful Communication in Groups and Teams**. New York, NY: iUniverse, 2013.

Harris, Dan. **10% Happier: How I Tamed the Voice in My Head, Reduced Stress Without Losing My Edge, and Found Self-Help That Actually Works—A True Story**. New York, NY: Dey Street Books, 2014.

Kabat-Zinn, Jon. **Mindfulness for Beginners: Reclaiming the Present Moment and Your Life**. Boulder, CO: Sounds True, 2016.

Katzenbach, Jon R., and Douglas K. Smith. **The Wisdom of Teams: Creating the High-Performance Organization**. Boston, MA: Harvard Business Review Press, 2015.

Scott, S. J. **S.M.A.R.T. Goals Made Simple: 10 Steps to Master Your Personal and Career Goals**. Read by Matt Stone. S.J. Scott, 2014. Audiobook.

CHAPTER 4: DRIVE FOR YES

Fisher, Roger C., William Ury, and Bruce Patton. **Getting to Yes: Negotiating Agreement Without Giving In**. New York, NY: Penguin, 2011.

Schwarz, Roger M., Anne Davidson, Peg Carlson, and Sue McKinney. **The Skilled Facilitator Fieldbook: Tips, Tools, and Tested Methods for Consultants, Facilitators, Managers, Trainers, and Coaches**. San Francisco, CA: Jossey-Bass, 2005.

Senge, Peter, Charlotte Roberts, Richard B. Ross, Bryan Smith, and Art Kleiner. **The Fifth Discipline Fieldbook: Strategies and Tools for Building a Learning Organization**. London: Nicholas Brealey, 2009.

CHAPTER 5: FEEL THE DIFFERENCE

Carroll, Michael. **Awake at Work: Facing the Challenges of Life on the Job**. Boulder, CO: Shambhala Publications, 2005.

Carroll, Michael. **The Mindful Leader**. Boston, MA: Trumpeter, 2008.

Goleman, Daniel. **Focus: The Hidden Driver of Excellence**. New York, NY: Harper, 2015.

Heider, John. **The Tao of Leadership**. Palm Beach, FL: Green Dragon Books, 2015.

STEPHEN GAY

Stephen Gay is a passionate and creative design leader in the Bay Area. Stephen takes pride in nurturing high-performing teams to solve complex problems and deliver innovative, simple, and delightful experiences.

DER-SHING HELMER

Der-shing Helmer is a game and comic artist living in the California Bay Area. She has a formal background in science and education, and an informal one in art, and enjoys making comics whenever possible.

MATT SILADY

A Chicagoland native, Matt Silady taught eighth grade for six years in Champaign, Illinois, before moving west to study creative writing at the University of California at Davis. It was there he discovered comics as a medium for fine art.

RON KERTZNER

Ron Kertzner supports individuals, teams, and organizations in acting from a deeply-held purpose and vision that is empowering to all. Ron serves as a facilitative consultant, helping organizations and teams gain clarity around their vision, organizational culture, and strategy.